The Ladybird Hunt

by Alison Norman

Grandad was cross! Greenfly were eating his roses.

Greenfly are very small green insects. They feed on the juice inside the leaves of plants. One greenfly mother can have lots of babies, so a plant is soon covered in hungry greenfly.

He sent Sam to look for some ladybirds.

Ladybirds are beetles. The ladybirds that Sam is looking for have shiny red backs with seven black spots on them. They eat greenfly. So do young ladybirds, called *larvae*.

Sam looked in the grass,

4

but all he found was a hurrying
ant.

Ants dig tunnels in the ground in which to live. They
live and work together in a big family called a
colony.

He looked in the hedge,

but all he found was a spider
spinning a sticky web.

Spiders have eight legs. The garden spider pulls
threads of silk from its body to make a sticky web.
The web is a trap to catch small animals like flies
for the spider to eat.

He looked under a stone,

but all he found was a shiny
black beetle.

This beetle is called a ground beetle. It hunts at
night for small creatures to eat. In the daytime it
hides in a damp, dark place. Ground beetles have
six long legs and they can run very fast.

He looked amongst the leaves,

but all he found was a soft green caterpillar.

This caterpillar hatched out of a tiny egg laid by a small white butterfly. It will eat the cabbages and grow fat. When it has finished growing as a caterpillar it will make a hard case called a *pupa*. Inside the pupa the caterpillar will change into a butterfly. Can you see some eggs, caterpillars, pupas and butterflies in this picture?

He looked under a bush,

but all he found was a woodlouse who rolled into a ball.

Woodlice live in damp, dark places. They come out at night to eat dead plants. Woodlice have 16 legs and some kinds can roll up into a ball if they are frightened.

Sam went back to Grandad and the roses. He could see the greenfly and...

...ladybirds! The ladybirds had found the greenfly.

Ladybirds are not the only animals that will eat the greenfly. Lacewings eat greenfly too, and so do some birds.

How many animals can you spot that will help Grandad to get rid of the greenfly?

Index